Handling data

ENTRY LEVEL 2

Jayne Garner
Joy Collins

ISBN 978-1-84618-263-1

Axis Education, PO Box 459
Shrewsbury SY4 4WZ.
email: enquiries@axiseducation.co.uk
www.axiseducation.co.uk

First published September 2003
Second edition (revised and reset) 2006
Third edition 2008
Fourth edition 2011

Contents

Introduction   v

Teaching notes
Worksheets 1, 10, 11   vii
Worksheets 2, 3, 17, 22, 23, 24, 36, 41, 42, 49   vii
Worksheets 4, 5, 14, 23, 25, 33, 48   vii
Worksheets 6, 7, 26, 27, 38, 39, 50, 51   viii
Worksheets 8, 9, 18, 21, 24, 29, 30, 31, 32, 33, 35, 37, 49   viii
Worksheets 12, 13, 15, 16, 17, 19, 21, 22, 29, 30, 31, 36, 37, 42, 49   ix
Worksheets 20, 28, 35, 37, 40, 43   ix
Worksheets 21, 31, 36, 42   ix
Worksheets 32, 34, 44   ix
Worksheets 35, 43, 46, 47   x

Student checklist   xi

Photocopiable worksheets
1. Data handling
2. How to read table
3. How to read table
4. How to read inforr block graphs
5. How to read inforn block graphs
6. Where can it go? 1
7. Where can it go? 2
8. Data everywhere 1
9. Data everywhere 2
10. Show it off 1
11. Show it off 2
12. How to label a block
13. How to construct a bl
14. Hotel – guest survey   14
15. Hotel – laundry bar chart   15
16. Hotel – housekeeping bar chart   16
17. Hotel – keeping the customers happy   17
18. Hotel – leisure club use 1   18
19. Hotel – leisure club use 2   19
20. Hotel – the mystery tour   20
21. Hotel – keep fit classes   21
22. Hotel – lunch menu 1   22
23. Hotel – lunch menu 2   23
24. Hotel – lunch survey 1   24
25. Hotel – lunch survey 2   25
26. Hotel – sorting people   26

27. Hotel – organising rooms   27
28. Supermarket – staff training   28
29. Supermarket – daily dairy count   29
30. Supermarket – daily toiletries count   30
31. Supermarket – daily groceries count   31
32. Supermarket – frozen favourites   32
33. Supermarket – staffing   33
34. Supermarket – sales figure   34
35. Supermarket – sun protection   35
36. Supermarket – movie magic   36
37. Supermarket – buying music   37
38. Supermarket – sorting people   38
39. Supermarket – organising returns   39
40. Factory – staff training   40
41. Factory – who works the most?   41
42. Factory – top of the league   42
43. Factory – league fixtures   43
44. Factory – distance from work   44
45. F… ransport to work   45
… anteen menu 1   46
… anteen menu 2   47
… ending machine sales   48
… ock check   49
… rting people   50
… ganising parts   51

52

62

trix   63

Introduction

Functional Skillbuilders have been specifically developed to support teachers delivering Functional Skills and the Skills for Life framework in Adult Literacy and Numeracy. There are 32 volumes in the series providing a dedicated Functional Skillbuilder volume for each section and level of the Functional Skills standards/Adult Literacy and Numeracy Curricula. There are 2 IT volumes at Levels 1 and 2.

All the activities in Functional Skillbuilders are based in three workplace settings – a hotel, a supermarket and a factory. This helps make the activities both real and relevant to adult and young adult learners. Knowledge about each workplace builds cumulatively as students progress through the levels. The tasks become increasingly work specific as students progress through the series. Students will find the tasks in Entry Level 2 Handling Data straightforward.

Functional Skills

These activities are task-based and provide teachers with a variety of materials to build the full range of Functional Maths skills relating to handling data. The first section of the book explicitly teaches the functional handling data skills required at Entry Level 2. Students then have 2–3 more opportunities to build and apply these skills in vocational contexts, allowing the teacher to teach skills, enable practise and to check learning. We have chosen to introduce the term 'axis' in this title.

Functional Skillbuilders are designed to be mediated by teachers. The teaching notes explain the skills addressed on each worksheet and provide guidance for teaching strategies. Teaching materials have also been included. There are alphabet and number cue cards at the lower levels. Templates for group work are included at every level.

How to use this pack

Ask the student to complete the checklist on page xi with you. This checklist will tell you the handling data skills your student most wants to practise. Use the outcome of this discussion to agree targets with the student and use the table to identify suitable worksheets.

Teaching notes

There are teaching notes for each worksheet. They explain the purpose of each worksheet and any groundwork that the teacher needs to cover first. The teaching notes include suggestions for group work, work in pairs and extension work.

Worksheets

A box like this at the top of each worksheet tells students the skills they will practise, ensuring that they are aware of learning outcomes from the outset.

Teaching point

 If there are any teaching points on the worksheet they will appear like this.

Tutor questions

tutor questions

Questions to be read aloud by the teacher appear at the bottom of the worksheet in a box like this.

Curriculum elements matrix

For ready reference by the teacher, a matrix of adult core curriculum elements mapped to all the worksheets is provided on page 63. Mapping to the Functional Skills standards is available electronically. Please email enquiries@axiseducation.co.uk.

Additional teaching materials

Templates for group work are at the very back of the pack. Photocopy them as required.

These teaching notes are organised by worksheet. There are teaching notes for every worksheet and they are designed to be read in conjunction with a photocopy of the relevant worksheet. The skills covered map to the **Student checklist** on page xi of this pack. The Groundwork section highlights the skills that need to be taught before your students tackle the worksheets, together with teaching suggestions. Suggestions for paired and group work are also included, where appropriate.

Worksheets 1, 10, 11
Represent data so that it makes sense

Groundwork

The information on the teaching points of these worksheets underpins many of the exercises throughout this book. The purpose of these worksheets is to familiarise students with methods of presenting data. You should discuss each method and explain how different methods suit different sets of data.

Worksheets

Read through the information on the worksheets with your students.

Worksheets 2, 3, 17, 22, 23, 25, 36, 41, 42, 49
Extract information from tables

Groundwork

Use the teaching point on each worksheet to explain how to extract information from tables. Make sure that your students understand the terms *row* and *column*.

Worksheets

Explain the skills your students are going to practise, then read the instructions to them. These worksheets are similar activities requiring students to extract information from tables contextualised to the hotel, supermarket and factory. You could use a selection of worksheets to *teach*, a selection to *reinforce* and a selection to *check* your students' ability to extract information from tables.

Group work

Tables from Worksheets 22 and 41 are available as Templates 1 and 2. Use the templates to conduct these exercises as group activities.

Extension work

Source a selection of straightforward tables. Use the lists as source material for extracting information. You could combine the handling data aspect with recognising numbers – ask students to track the texts and highlight all the numbers they can find.

Worksheets 4, 5, 14, 23, 25, 33, 48
Extract information from bar charts (block graphs)

Groundwork

Use the teaching point on Worksheet 4 to explain how to extract information from bar charts. Make sure that your students understand the terms *axis*, *column* and *title*.

Worksheets 4, 5

Explain the skills your students are going to practise, then read the instructions to them and ask them to answer the questions.

Teaching notes

Worksheets 14, 23, 25, 33, 48

These worksheets are similar activities requiring students to extract information from bar charts contextualised to the hotel, supermarket and factory. You could use Worksheet 14 to *teach*, Worksheets 23 and 25 to *reinforce* and Worksheets 33 and 48 to *check* your students' ability to extract information from bar charts.

Group work

Bar charts from Worksheets 14 and 33 are available as Templates 3 and 4. Use the templates to conduct these exercises as group activities.

Extension work

You could extend these activities by showing students a bar chart that has columns of unequal widths – how does this skew the data? You could also prepare two bar charts providing the same set of data with the axes swapped over. Does this affect their understanding of the data?

Worksheets 6, 7, 26, 27, 38, 39, 50, 51
Sort and classify objects

Groundwork

Use the teaching point on Worksheet 6 to explain how to sort and classify objects according to two *criteria*.

Worksheets

Explain the skills your students are going to practise, then read the instructions to them. These worksheets are similar activities requiring students to sort and classify objects contextualised to the hotel, supermarket and factory. You could use Worksheets 26 and 27 to *teach*, Worksheets 38 and 39 to *reinforce* and Worksheets 50 and 51 to *check* your students'

ability to sort and classify objects using two criteria.

Group work

Data from Worksheets 38 and 51 are available as Templates 5 and 6. Use the templates to conduct these exercises as group activities.

Extension work

Source a selection of tangible objects for students to sort and classify using two criteria. These could include:

- items costing more or less than £1 from different sections of a supermarket

- items – by colour and size

- laundry – machine wash or hand wash, and at what temperature.

Worksheets 8, 9, 18, 21, 24, 29, 30, 31, 32, 33, 35, 37, 49
Collect data

Groundwork

Use the teaching point on Worksheet 8 to explain how to count tally marks. The teaching point on Worksheet 9 shows students how to log data in a simple grid.

Worksheets

Explain the skills your students are going to practise, then read the instructions to them. These worksheets are similar activities requiring students to collect data contextualised to the hotel, supermarket and factory. You could use a selection of worksheets to *teach*, a selection of worksheets to *reinforce* and a selection of worksheets to *check* your students' ability to collect data.

Extension work

Ask students to gather and present information on topics of their own choice. Help them to formulate clear questions before going ahead with their data collection.

Worksheets 12, 13, 15, 16, 17, 19, 22, 29, 30, 37, 49
Construct bar charts (block graphs)

Groundwork

Remind your students about the need to present data clearly. They will need to decide which way to present the axes. Provide A4 centimetre-squared paper to make these tasks easier.

Worksheets

Ask students to construct bar charts using the data provided. These worksheets are similar activities requiring students to construct bar charts contextualised to the hotel, supermarket and factory. You could use a selection of worksheets to *teach*, a selection of worksheets to *reinforce* and a selection of worksheets to *check* your students' ability to construct bar charts.

Worksheets 20, 28, 35, 37, 40, 43
Present data in a table

Groundwork

Remind your students about the need to present data clearly.

Worksheets

Ask students to complete the tables using the data provided. These worksheets are similar activities requiring students to present data in a table contextualised to the hotel, supermarket and factory. You could use Worksheets 20 and

28 to *teach*, Worksheets 35 and 37 to *reinforce* and Worksheets 40 and 43 to *check* your students' ability to present data in a table.

Worksheets 21, 31, 36, 42
Present data in a pictogram

Groundwork

Remind your students about the need to present data clearly. They will need to choose an icon to represent each category and decide how much each icon represents. Students should provide a key with each pictogram.

Worksheets

Ask students to construct pictograms using the data provided. These worksheets are similar activities requiring students to construct pictograms contextualised to the hotel, supermarket and factory. You could use a selection of worksheets to *teach*, a selection of worksheets to *reinforce* and a selection of worksheets to *check* your students' ability to construct pictograms.

Worksheets 32, 34, 44
Extract information from pictograms

Groundwork

Show your students the icon in each of the pictograms and make sure they are aware of the number each icon represents.

Worksheets

Explain the skills your students are going to practise, then read the instructions to them. These worksheets are similar activities requiring students to extract information from pictograms contextualised to the supermarket and factory. You could use Worksheet 32 to *teach*, Worksheet

34 to *reinforce* and Worksheet 44 to *check* your students' ability to extract information from pictograms.

Worksheets 35, 43, 46, 47
Extract information from lists

Worksheets

Explain the skills your students are going to practise, then read the instructions to them.

Extension work

Source a selection of straightforward lists. Use the lists as source material for extracting information.

Student checklist

Functional Skillbuilders Handling Data Entry Level 2 will help you improve your Functional Maths skills. This chart lists the data handling skills covered in this book. Tick the boxes to say which skills you think you will find the most useful to practise. Then discuss your ideas with your tutor.

Skill	✔	Worksheets
Carry out a survey		9, 24, 32, 33, 35, 37
Construct a block graph		15, 16, 17, 19, 22, 24, 29, 30, 32, 33, 37, 49
Count tally marks		18, 21, 29, 30, 31, 49
Extract data from lists		26, 27, 38, 43, 50
Extract data from price lists		35, 46, 47
Extract data from block graphs/bar charts		4, 5, 14, 23, 25, 33, 45, 48
Extract data from pictograms		32, 33, 44
Extract data from tables		2, 3, 17, 21, 22, 23, 25, 36, 41, 42, 49
Give a block graph a title		13
Label axes on a block graph		12
Present data in a pictogram		21, 31, 36, 42
Present data in a table		24, 32, 33, 35, 37, 43
Present data in a timetable		20, 28, 40
Sort and classify objects using two criteria		6, 7, 26, 27, 38, 39, 50, 51
Understand different ways to present data		1, 10, 11
Use a tally chart to collect data		8, 9, 18, 21, 29

1. Data handling

Represent information so that it makes sense.

Data can be thought of as another word for *information*. You can gather data on just about anything. But data can be a bit boring, so the way you present it is important.

Data looks best if you use pictures or graphics. Using colour can help make the data easier to understand.

Data can be presented in:
1. Lists
2. Block graphs/bar charts
3. Tables
4. Diagrams
5. Pictograms

1

Birthday list
1. Dad   1st January
2. Ken   3rd February
3. Ann   22nd April
4. Nan   4th June
5. Bill   7th July
6. Mum   18th July

2

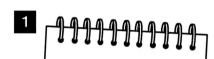

Modes of transport of work

(Bar chart: Number of staff vs Modes of transport — Car ≈ 30, Bicycle ≈ 11, Train ≈ 26, Bus ≈ 22, Walk ≈ 17)

3

	Downloads	CDs
Pop	20	3
Country and western	15	1
Classical	5	1
Heavy metal	8	2

4

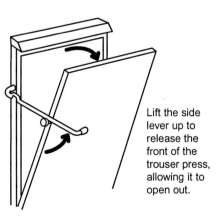

Lift the side lever up to release the front of the trouser press, allowing it to open out.

5

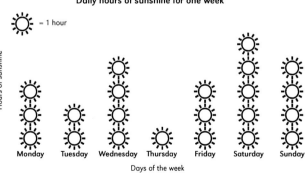

Daily hours of sunshine for one week

☀ = 1 hour

(Pictogram showing hours of sunshine for Monday, Tuesday, Wednesday, Thursday, Friday, Saturday, Sunday)

The way you choose to show off the data is up to you – but some ways are better than others for showing your data to its best advantage.

Extract information from tables.

A table is only one way of showing data (information). You have to follow some very simple rules when working with tables. Tables are made up of *rows* (which go across) and *columns* (which go down). Look at this table showing the cost of posting parcels.

This table has nine rows, including the header, and two columns.

To use this table you have to "read" down the columns and across the rows.

— columns —

Weight – up to:	Cost
1 kg	£2.50
2 kg	£3.50
3 kg	£4.50
4 kg	£5.50
5 kg	£6.50
6 kg	£7.50
7 kg	£8.50
8 kg	£9.50

rows

This table tells you know how much it will cost to send parcels that weigh between 0 kg and 8 kg by courier. Use the information in the table to fill in the gaps.

1. It will cost _____ to send a parcel weighing 4 kg.

2. It will cost _____ to send a parcel weighing 3 kg.

3. It will cost _____ to send a parcel weighing 8 kg.

4. It will cost _____ to send a parcel weighing 6 kg.

5. It will cost _____ to send a parcel weighing 7 kg.

6. It will cost _____ to send a parcel weighing 5 kg.

Extract information from tables.

Weight – up to:	Cost
1 kg	£2.50
2 kg	£3.50
3 kg	£4.50
4 kg	£5.50
5 kg	£6.50
6 kg	£7.50
7 kg	£8.50
8 kg	£9.50

Use the table to answer these questions.

1. How much will a parcel weigh if it costs £7.50 to post? _____

2. How much will a parcel weigh if it costs £2.50 to post? _____

3. How much will a parcel weigh if it costs £5.50 to post? _____

4. How much will a parcel weigh if it costs £8.50 to post? _____

5. How much will a parcel weigh if it costs £4.50 to post? _____

6. How much will a parcel weigh if it costs £9.50 to post? _____

7. How much will a parcel weigh if it costs £3.50 to post? _____

8. How much will a parcel weigh if it costs £6.50 to post? _____

	Extract information from block graphs.

A block graph is another way of showing data (information). Block graphs are made up of blocks (columns) which sit on an axis. Block graphs are also known as *bar charts*.

This block graph shows the results of a survey carried out in the factory's canteen. It shows the most popular crisp flavours.

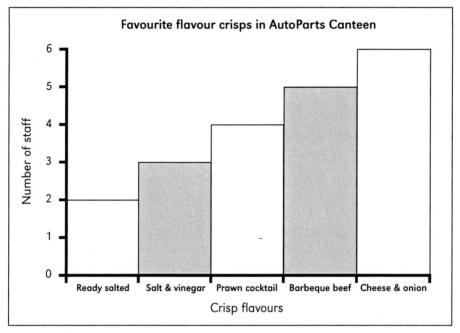

Block graphs should:
- be drawn carefully using a ruler
- always have a title
- have the axes clearly labelled.

The blocks can be shaded or coloured to make the data clearer if necessary.

This block graph tells us that:
- two people surveyed preferred ready salted crisps.
- three people surveyed preferred salt and vinegar crisps.
- four people surveyed preferred prawn cocktail crisps.
- five people surveyed preferred barbeque beef crisps.
- six people surveyed preferred cheese and onion crisps.

You can use this data to conclude that:
- ready salted crisps were the least favourite flavour
- cheese and onion were the favourite flavour crisps.

| Extract information from block graphs. |

This block graph shows the results of a survey which asked people who work at Blackwell's Supermarket how they travel to work. Use the information in the block graph to answer the questions.

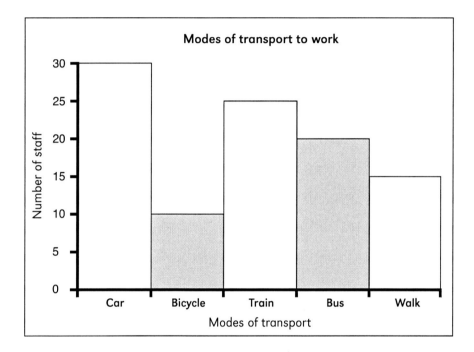

1. How many people walk to work? _____

2. How many people catch the bus to work? _____

3. How many people use the train to get to work? _____

4. How many people drive to work? _____

5. How many people cycle to work? _____

6. Which is the most popular method of transport?_____

7. Which is the least popular method of transport? _____

6. Where can it go? 1

Sort and classify objects using two criteria.

One part of handling data is to sort things into categories. Some things are easier to sort than others!

Look at this selection of homeware items.

They could be sorted into:

                Crockery   Cutlery   Glasses

But if you had to sort out lots of hardware, you might sort them into:

                Knives   Forks   Spoons

                Wines glasses   Brandy glasses Tumblers

So, it depends on what the items are and how many you have to sort as to what criteria you choose to sort them into.

Sort and classify objects using two criteria.

These objects can be sorted using two criteria – their size and shape. Count the number of shapes using the criteria in the tables.

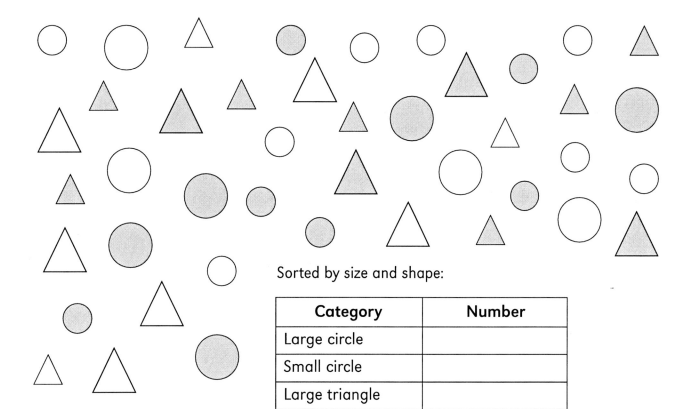

Sorted by size and shape:

Category	Number
Large circle	
Small circle	
Large triangle	
Small triangle	

Sorted by size and colour:

Category	Number
Large shaded	
Small shaded	

Sorted by shape and colour:

Category	Number
Shaded circle	
Un-shaded circle	
Shaded triangle	
Un-shaded triangle	

Which do you think is the best way to sort these shapes and why?

Collect data.

Data can be collected in a number of different ways. One of the most common ways is to carry out a survey. In surveys you either count things yourself or ask people questions and note their answers. Questions in a survey need to be phrased to give very clear answers – either a "yes" or "no", or a simple one-word answer.

There are a number of ways of recording the data you collect in your survey. One of the most simple is to make a *tally chart*. A tally mark is simply a small line for each answer.

When you have written four tallies, the fifth is written as a stroke through the other four. This is sometimes called a *five bar gate*.

| = 1 || = 2 ||| = 3 |||| = 4   ℕℕ = 5

This tally chart records the number of people in a group who are smokers or non-smokers.

Smoker	ℕℕ ||	7
Non-smoker	ℕℕ ℕℕ ||	12

Work out the totals for each of these tally charts.

1

Married	ℕℕ ||||	
Single	ℕℕ ℕℕ |||	

2

Male	ℕℕ ℕℕ ℕℕ	
Female	ℕℕ ℕℕ |||	

3

Driver	ℕℕ ||||	
Non-driver	ℕℕ ||	

4

Employed	ℕℕ ℕℕ ||||	
Not employed	ℕℕ ||	

Collect data.

Another way to collect data is to prepare a simple grid before you do the survey so that you can write answers directly into it.

Use these grids to carry out surveys among a set of people.

1. Shoe size survey

	3	4	5	6	7	8	9	10	11
Number									

2. Number of hours spent watching television each week

	0–5	6–10	11–15	16–20	21–24	25–30	30+
Number							

3. Number of hours spent travelling to work each week

	3	4	5	6	6+
Number					

4. Number of holidays taken last year

	0	1	2	3	4	4+
Number						

5. Number of brothers and sisters

	0	1	2	3	4	5	6	7
Number								

Whichever way you choose to collect your data, it is important that you have a clear set of figures to use when presenting your data.

Choose the best way to show off your data.

There is a range of ways of presenting your data. The method you select is up to you – but some ways are better than others for showing certain types of data to the best advantage.

Lists

Lists are good for presenting certain types of data. A list is useful if you need to do things in a certain order or have a lot of things to do in a day. It can be useful to tick off each job as you do it.

Birthday list
1. Dad   1st January
2. Ken   3rd February
3. Ann   22nd April
4. Nan   4th June
5. Bill   7th July
6. Mum 18th July

Tables

Tables are great for presenting some forms of data. They are ideal for showing a rota of jobs, for example who has to do what on each day of the week.

	Monday	Tuesday	Wednesday	Thursday	Friday
Tom	✔		✔		
Dick		✔			✔
Harry				✔	

A table would be a good way of showing the highest temperatures reached on each day of the week.

	Monday	Tuesday	Wednesday	Thursday	Friday
Temps	18°C	21°C	24°C	19°C	20°C

Pictograms

Pictograms are made up of pictures. A simple picture or symbol is chosen to show a number of responses in a survey. A graph is built using the symbols to show how many people responded to certain questions. This pictogram shows the number of people who drive to work in each department.

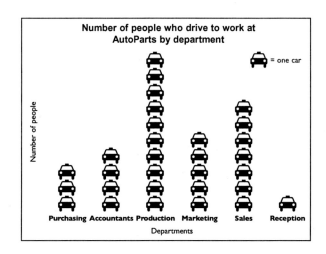

Choose the best way to show off your data.

Block or bar graph

A block graph has two axes, a *vertical axis* (which goes up) and a *horizontal axis* (which goes across). Both the axes should be labelled. The data is represented on one axis and the frequency on the other.

Bar charts can consist of either horizontal or vertical bars. It is important to make each bar the same width so that the graph does not look misleading.

Bar charts make comparing data easy.

This block graph shows the results of a survey to find out which drink people prefer first thing in the morning.

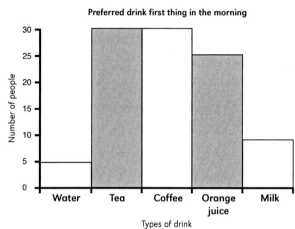

Diagrams

A diagram is a good way to display things that need to be explained using a graphic, for example the layout of a room or a building. If you have to give directions, a diagram (map) may be the best way.

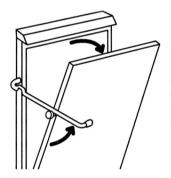

Lift the side lever up to release the front of the trouser press, allowing it to open out.

State the best method to present these types of data.

1. Directions to your home   _____

2. A set of tasks you need to complete today   _____

3. Library opening times   _____

4. The results of a survey showing the number of smokers
    compared to non-smokers   _____

5. A set of instructions for using a toaster   _____

Label the axes on a block graph.

A block graph, or bar chart, has two axes, a vertical and a horizontal one. The axes should be labelled. The data is represented on one axis and the frequency on the other.

Look at these three block graphs. The axes have not been labelled. Choose the correct label from the box and write the labels in the spaces.

1

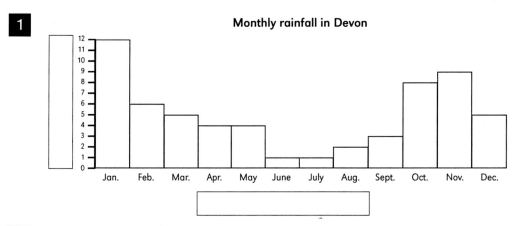

Monthly rainfall in Devon

2

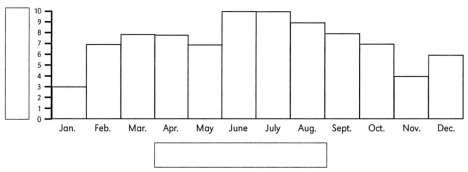

Average hours of daily sunshine in each month in Devon

3

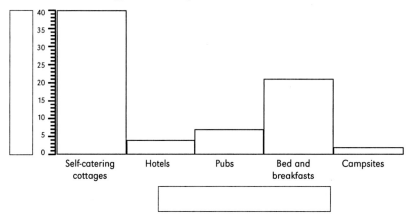

Types of holiday accommodation available near Yelverton

Axis titles

Months

Centimetres

Months

Hours

Number of

Accommodation

13. How to construct a block graph

Give block graphs suitable titles.

None of these block graphs have titles. Read the information and choose a suitable title from the selection provided.

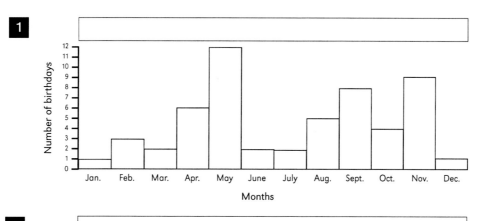

1

Number of birthdays (y-axis, 0–12)

Months (x-axis: Jan., Feb., Mar., Apr., May, June, July, Aug., Sept., Oct., Nov., Dec.)

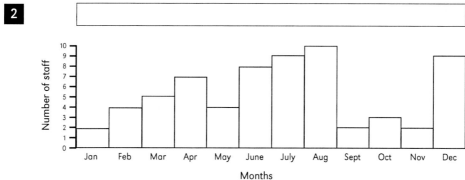

2

Number of staff (y-axis, 0–10)

Months (x-axis: Jan, Feb, Mar, Apr, May, June, July, Aug, Sept, Oct, Nov, Dec)

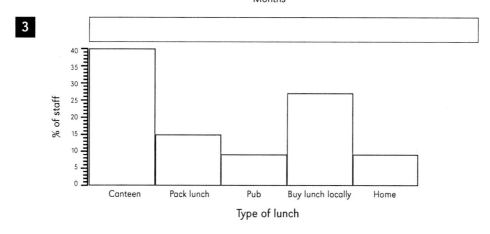

3

% of staff (y-axis, 0–40)

Type of lunch (x-axis: Canteen, Pack lunch, Pub, Buy lunch locally, Home)

Staff's lunchtime habits over a month
Number of staff on holiday each month
Number of staff birthdays per month

Extract information and make comparisons from block graphs.

Use the data in this block graph to answer the questions.

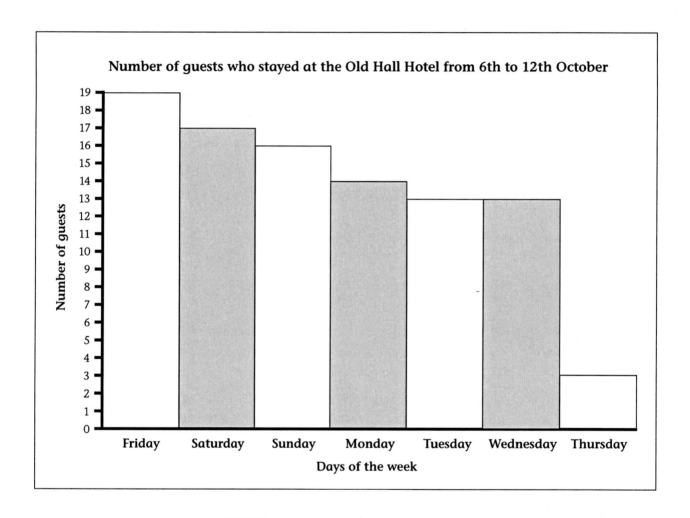

Number of guests who stayed at the Old Hall Hotel from 6th to 12th October

tutor questions

1. What is the title of this chart?

2. How many people stayed on Sunday?

3. Which was the most popular night to stay?

4. What was the least popular night to stay?

5. How many more people stayed on Saturday than on Wednesday?

6. On which two nights did the same number of guests stay?

Construct a bar chart.

These are the items that were sent to the laundry last Monday. Count each set of items and use a sheet of A4 centimetre-squared paper to construct a bar chart to display the data. Remember to give your chart a heading and to label the axes.

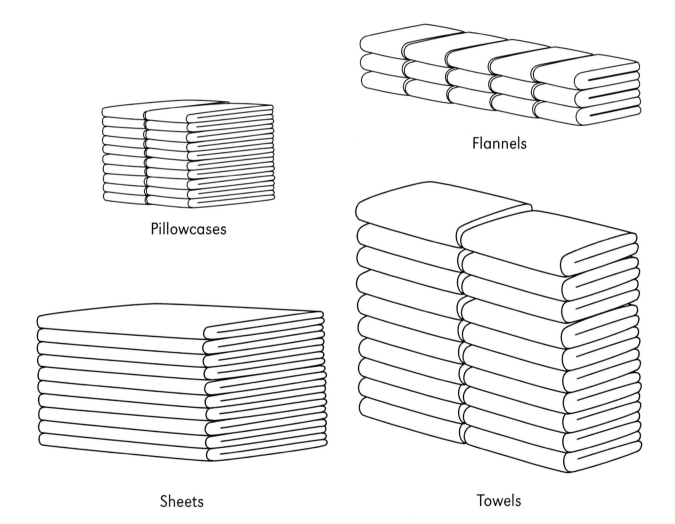

Flannels

Pillowcases

Sheets

Towels

Construct a bar chart.

These are the toiletry items that the housekeeper ordered last week. Count each set of items and use a sheet of A4 centimetre-squared paper to construct a bar chart to display the data. Remember to give your chart a heading and to label the axes.

17. Hotel – keeping the customers happy

Extract information from a table. Construct a bar chart.

When guests check out of the hotel, they are asked to fill in a questionnaire. This helps the Old Hall Hotel improve its services. Guests tick the things they are happy with and write a note about the items they are not happy with. This table is a summary of the questionnaires from guests who checked out on Saturday 14 December.

Guest	Room size	Cleanliness	Room service	Meals	Value for money	Porter service	Would you revisit?
Guest 1		✔	✔	✔	✔		✔
Guest 2	✔	✔	✔	✔	✔	✔	✔
Guest 3	✔	✔	✔	✔		✔	✔
Guest 4	✔	✔	✔	✔	✔	✔	✔
Guest 5		✔	✔	✔	✔		✔
Guest 6	✔	✔	✔	✔	✔	✔	✔
Guest 7	✔	✔	✔	✔		✔	✔
Guest 8		✔	✔	✔	✔	✔	✔
Guest 9	✔	✔	✔	✔	✔		✔

1. Count all the ticks and write the total in each box.

Guest	Room size	Cleanliness	Room service	Meals	Value for money	Porter service	Would you revisit?
Totals							

2. Draw a bar chart (block graph) to show these results. Give your chart a suitable title and label each axis.

skilbuild

Collect data. Count tally marks.

Each week, the leisure club receptionist keeps a record of how many guests use the facilities. She uses a tally chart. When someone uses part of the leisure club, a sheet is marked with a |.

Count up the tallies for each day and write the total for each leisure facility in the box.

	Pool	Jacuzzi	Sauna	Weights	Studio
Monday	||| ||| ||| ||	||| ||||	||| ||||	||||	||
Tuesday	||| ||||	||| ||	||| ||	|||	
Wednesday	||| ||||	||| |||	||||		
Thursday	||| ||||	||| ||||	||| ||	|||	
Friday	||| ||| ||| ||||	||| ||| ||||	||| ||||	||| ||||	||||
Saturday	||| ||| ||| |||	||| ||| ||| ||	||| ||| |||	||| ||| |||		||| ||| ||| ||||
Sunday	||| ||| ||||	||| ||||	||| ||| |||		||| ||	||||

	Pool	Jacuzzi	Sauna	Weights	Studio
Monday					
Tuesday					
Wednesday					
Thursday					
Friday					
Saturday					
Sunday					

Construct block graphs.

This block graph shows how many guests used the leisure club facilities on Monday. Label each axis and give the graph a title.

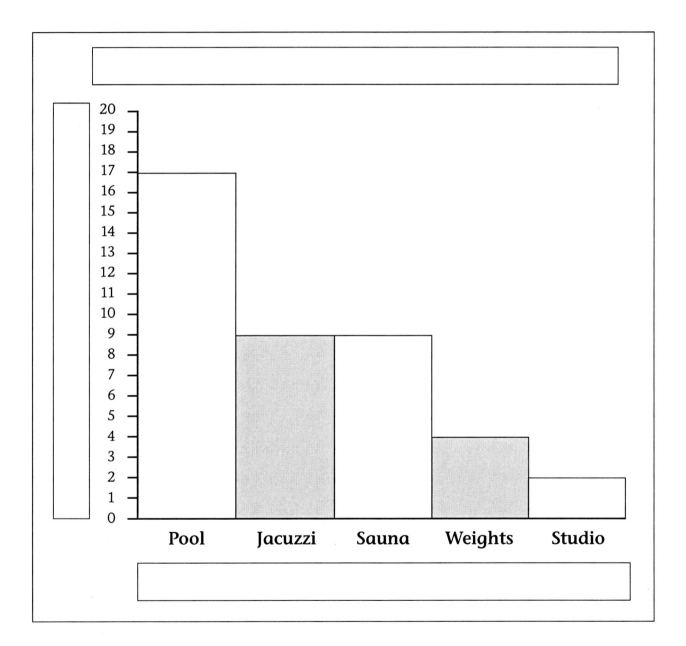

Now use centimetre-squared paper to construct block graphs to show how guests used the leisure club facilities on each of the other days. You should label each axis and give each graph a suitable title. You should produce six graphs in total.

20. Hotel – the mystery tour

Present data in a timetable.

The Old Hall Hotel arranges day trips for guests. One of the trips is a mystery tour. Transfer this information about the mystery tour into the table. The first entry has been done for you.

You meet in the hotel lobby at 9 in the morning. The driver will check your tickets. The bus leaves at quarter past 9. The journey will take about an hour. You will arrive at your destination at about quarter past 10. You will meet for lunch at noon. The bus will head back to the hotel at 3 o'clock. This means you will return to the hotel at about 4 o'clock.

Time	Action	Notes
9 a.m.	Meet in lobby	Check tickets
	Bus leaves	
	-	

Make a tally chart. Construct a pictogram.

This is a timetable of classes at the Old Hall Hotel leisure club. Count the activity types and make a tally chart for the frequency of each activity. Find the total number of aerobics, swimming and tennis sessions at the hotel.

	9–10 am	11–12 am	2–3 pm	4–5 pm
Monday	Aerobics	Tennis	Aerobics	Swimming
Tuesday	Swimming	Aerobics	Tennis	Aerobics
Wednesday	Aerobics	Swimming	Aerobics	Tennis
Thursday	Tennis	Aerobics	Swimming	Aerobics
Friday	Aerobics	Swimming	Aerobics	Tennis
Saturday	Swimming	Aerobics	Swimming	Aerobics
Sunday	Swimming	Tennis	Aerobics	Swimming

Activity	Tally	Total
Aerobics		
Swimming		
Tennis		

If each session lasts an hour, how many hours of aerobics, swimming and tennis are on offer at the hotel?

Aerobics	
Swimming	
Tennis	

Present the data from your tally chart as a pictogram using one of these symbols.

Extract data from a table. Construct a bar chart.

The chef at the Old Hall Hotel keeps a record of the number of meals ordered. This data shows how many people ordered each of the dishes from the lunch menu last week. Use the data to complete the table below.

	Grilled plaice	Cod and chips	Salmon supreme	Sausages and mash	Pork casserole
Monday	3	1	2	0	6
Tuesday	4	3	12	6	3
Wednesday	2	6	4	10	12
Thursday	10	3	7	5	8
Friday	4	3	7	10	10
Saturday	12	8	8	11	14
Sunday	16	12	9	6	18

Main meal	Total for the week
Grilled plaice	
Cod and chips	
Salmon supreme	
Sausages and mash	
Pork casserole	

Present the data from the table you have just completed as a block graph.

Extract data from a table and a bar chart.

23

Use the information in the bar chart and table you created for Worksheet 22 to answer these questions.

1. Which was the most popular dish of the week? _____

2. Which was the least popular dish of the week? _____

3. On which day did the restaurant serve the most lunches? _____

4. On which day did the restaurant serve the least lunches? _____

5. On which days did the restaurant serve the same number of lunches? _____

6. How many dishes of sausage and mash did the restaurant serve during the week? _____

7. How many dishes of grilled plaice did the restaurant serve during the week? _____

This data could be used for a number of purposes. Examine this list of possible uses and decide if you think the data could be used for each one or not. The first one has been done for you.

	Yes	No
1. Help the chef plan what produce he needs to order	✔	
2. Help the chef decide what puddings to prepare		
3. Help the restaurant manager plan how many waiters to employ		
4. Help customers to decide what to order		
5. Help the chef decide what meal to take off the menu		
6. Help the chef decide how large the portions should be		

Carry out a survey. Present the findings.

Find out how popular the meals from the Old Hall Hotel's lunch menu are. Show a copy of the Old Hall Hotel's lunch menu to 20 people and ask them to choose a main course and a pudding. Make a note of their answers. Present your data for the main course and pudding separately. Present one set of data as a bar chart and the other as a table.

Old Hall Hotel
Lunch menu

Main courses
Whole North Sea Plaice grilled with Lemon & Herbs **£10.95**
Deep Fried Goujons of North Sea Cod served with Chips
& Tartare Sauce **£10.50**
Poached Supreme of Scottish Salmon in a Dill Crème **£12.75**
Local Beef Sausages on Mashed Potatoes with an Onion Gravy **£12.25**
Bramfield Pork & Bramley Apple Casserole **£13.75**
~ all dishes are served with chips, a selection of vegetables or salad ~
Please see the blackboard for Chef's specials & today's vegetarian selection

Desserts
All priced at £4.95
Hot Pistachio Soufflé, Pistachio Ice Cream
Steamed Pear Pudding with Caramelised Apple & Calvados Custard
Warm Chocolate Brownie with home made Vanilla Pod Ice Cream
Plum & Port Compote with Creamed Rice Pudding
Mango Cheesecake on a Passion Fruit Coulis

Extract data from tables and bar charts.

Use the information in the bar chart and table you created for Worksheet 24 to answer these questions.

1. Which was the most popular main course? _____

2. Which was the least popular main course? _____

3. Which was the most popular pudding? _____

4. Which was the least popular pudding? _____

5. List the main courses in order of popularity, starting with the least popular first.

    1. _____

    2. _____

    3. _____

    4. _____

    5. _____

6. List the puddings in order of popularity, starting with the most popular first.

    1. _____

    2. _____

    3. _____

    4. _____

    5. _____

Sort and classify objects using two criteria.

This staff list is in alphabetical order. The personnel department needs to sort out the data according to which department each person works for and whether they are temporary or permanent members of the Old Hall Hotel staff. Use the information in the list to create a table to display this data.

Baines, Denise	Promotions manager	Sales team	Permanent
Boyer, Henri	Wine waiter	Restaurant	Permanent
Bromley, Maxine	Manager	Leisure club	Permanent
Callington, Edith	Housekeeper	Housekeeping	Permanent
Clarke, Tim	Management		Permanent
Falstaff, John	Waiter	Restaurant	Temporary
Fitzpatrick, Steve	Waiter	Restaurant	Permanent
Goodman, Julie	Personnel Manager		Permanent
Green, Liam	Wine Waiter	Restaurant	Permanent
Hardy, Alex	Cook	Kitchen	Permanent
Holland, Bob	Porter	Housekeeping	Permanent
Davies, Jack	Instructor	Leisure club	Permanent
Jenkins, Laura,	Beauty therapist	Leisure club	Temporary
Jones, Val	Chef	Kitchen	Temporary
Leblanc, Anthony	Receptionist	Front of house staff	Temporary
Lyons, Jo	Receptionist	Front of house staff	Permanent
Menendez, Juan	Bar manager	Bar	Permanent
Mullins, Debbie	Catering Manager	Restaurant	Permanent
Nedding, Dolly	Kitchen hand	Kitchen	Temporary
Nunn, Irene,	Cook	Kitchen	Permanent
Othen, Jen	Bar staff	Bar	Temporary
Pace, Julia	Cleaner	Housekeeping	Permanent
Patel, Dev	Bar staff	Bar	Permanent
Pezzey, Sarah	Waitress	Restaurant	Temporary
Potter, Linda	Waitress	Restaurant	Permanent
Roberts, Louise	Chambermaid	Housekeeping	Temporary
Smith, Kevin	Chef	Kitchen	Permanent
Smith, Valerie	Cleaner	Housekeeping	Temporary
Vautier, Jean-Claude	Chef	Kitchen	Permanent
Vine, Maureen	Cook	Kitchen	Permanent
Wall, Jane	Cook	Kitchen	Permanent
Wu, Li	Chambermaid	Housekeeping	Permanent

Sort and classify objects using two criteria.

All the rooms at the Old Hall Hotel have a view of either the gardens or the moors. There are four different types of room: double, family, single and twin. This is a list of the rooms by floor and in the annexe. You need to provide a new list of bedrooms by type and by the type of view available.

First floor

2 double bedrooms with moorland view

2 double bedrooms with garden view

1 single bedroom with moorland view

1 twin bedroom with garden view

1 family bedroom with garden view

1 family bedroom with moorland view.

Second floor

3 double bedrooms with moorland view

2 double bedrooms with garden view

1 single bedroom with garden view

1 twin bedroom with moorland view

Annexe

5 double bedrooms with moorland view

5 double bedrooms with garden view

2 single bedrooms with moorland view

2 single bedrooms with garden view

1 twin bedroom with garden view

2 family bedroom with garden view

1 family bedroom with moorland view

Represent information in a timetable.

Forty members of staff at Blackwell's Supermarket are going on a training day in Lancaster. The Personnel Manager sends all the staff a timetable. Transfer the information about the training to the table.

All staff should meet in the supermarket car park at 9 am. I will need to check you off the list as we have two coaches. The coaches will leave at quarter past 9. The journey will take about an hour. We will arrive at Lancashire County Training at about half past ten. The training begins at 11 am, but you need to register first. There is a lunch break between 1 and 2 pm. The training finishes at 4 pm. Please remember to collect your certificates as you leave. The coaches will head back home at quarter past four. We should be back at Blackwell's by half past five.

Time	Action	Notes

Contruct a bar chart. Count tally marks.

Every day the staff note how much of each item in their section has been sold. Here is some of the data from the deli section for Friday 9th November. Use the information to answer the questions.

Type of cheese	Kilos sold	Total
Cheddar	||||| ||||| ||||| ||	
Edam	||||| |||||	
Stilton	||||| ||||| ||||| ||||| ||||	
Ricotta	|||||		
Brie	||||| ||||| |||	

1. Total each tally up and write the total in the column.

2. Draw a block graph to show how many kilos of each cheese were sold on Friday 9th November. Give your graph a title. Make sure you label each axis.

Contruct a bar chart. Count tally marks.

Every day the staff note how much of each item in their section has been sold. Here is some of the data from the toiletries section for Friday 9th November. Use the information to carry out the tasks.

Type of shampoo	Bottles sold	Total
Blackwell's anti-dandruff	ⅢⅢ ⅢⅢ IIII	
Blackwell's frequent use	ⅢⅢ ⅢⅢ ⅢⅢ ⅢⅢ ⅢⅢ ⅢⅢ I	
Blackwell's medicated	ⅢⅢ IIII	
Blackwell's extra body	ⅢⅢ ⅢⅢ ⅢⅢ ⅢⅢ ⅢⅢ II	
Blackwell's supersoft	ⅢⅢ ⅢⅢ ⅢⅢ III	

1. Total each tally up and write the total in the column.

2. Draw a block graph to show how many bottles of each shampoo were sold on Friday 9th November. Give your graph a title. Make sure you label each axis.

Contruct a pictogram. Count tally marks.

Every day the staff note how much of each item in their section has been sold. Here is some of the data from the canned goods section for Friday 9th November. Use the information to carry out the tasks.

Type of soup	Cans sold	Total
Blackwell's chicken	⃥⃥ ⃥⃥ ⃥⃥ ⃥⃥ ⃥⃥ ⃥⃥ ⃥⃥ II	
Blackwell's tomato	⃥⃥ ⃥⃥ ⃥⃥ ⃥⃥ ⃥⃥ ⃥⃥ ⃥⃥ ⃥⃥ IIII	
Blackwell's mushroom	⃥⃥ ⃥⃥ ⃥⃥ ⃥⃥ ⃥⃥ I	
Blackwell's oxtail	⃥⃥ ⃥⃥ ⃥⃥ ⃥⃥ III	
Blackwell's French onion	⃥⃥ ⃥⃥ ⃥⃥ ⃥⃥ ⃥⃥ I	

1. Total each tally up and write the total in the column.

2. Draw a pictogram to show how many cans of each soup were sold on Friday 9th November. Give your graph a title. Choose one of these icons to represent a can of soup.

Extract information from pictograms. Collect and present data.

Use the information from this pictogram to answer the questions.

Number of cartons of Blackwell's own brand of ice cream sold on 4th July

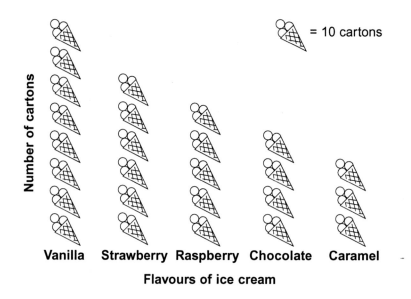

```
tutor questions
```

1. What is the title of the pictogram?

2. How many flavours of Blackwell's own-brand ice cream are there?

3. How many cartons of vanilla ice cream were sold?

4. How many more cartons of strawberry were sold than caramel?

5. How many fewer cartons of chocolate were sold than raspberry?

6. How many cartons of chocolate ice cream were sold?

7. How many fewer cartons of caramel were sold than vanilla?

8. How many cartons of ice cream were sold in total?

Carry out a survey like this with your friends, family or co-workers. Ask them to tell you their preferred flavour of ice cream. Display your findings as either a table or a block graph.

Extract information from bar charts. Collect and present data.

Use the information from this block graph to answer the questions.

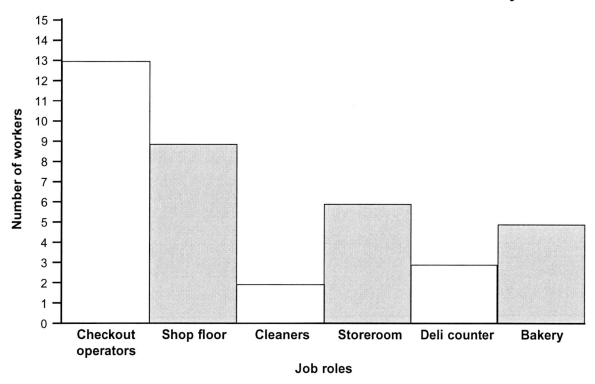

Number of workers in-store at 10 am on 27th July

tutor questions

1. What is the title of the graph?
2. How many job roles are listed?
3. How many people were working on the checkouts?
4. How many people were working in the bakery section?
5. How many fewer cleaners are there than deli section workers?
6. How many more cleaners are there than bakery section workers?
7. How many people work in the storeroom?

Carry out a survey like this with your friends, family or co-workers to find out what jobs they have or have had. Display your findings as either a table or a block graph.

Extract information from pictograms.

Use the information from this pictogram to answer the questions.

Sales figures for 14th October

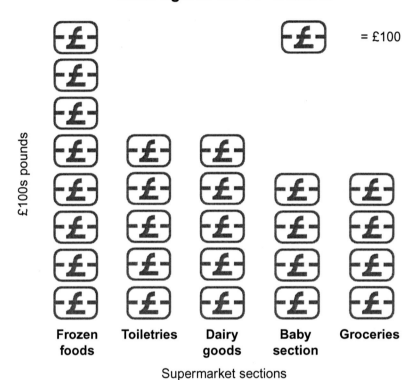

= £100

£100s pounds

Frozen foods   Toiletries   Dairy goods   Baby section   Groceries

Supermarket sections

tutor questions

1. What information does the pictogram give you?
2. What does "£" represent?
3. How many £100s were spent on toiletries on 14th October?
4. How many more £100s were spent on toiletries than groceries on 14th October?
5. How many £100s were spent on frozen food on 14th October?
6. How many more £100s were spent on frozen food than on dairy goods on 14th October?
7. How many £100s were spent on baby goods on 14th October?
8. How many £100s were spent altogether on 14th October?

Extract information from lists. Collect and present information.

This leaflet shows the prices of some of the sun protection products sold in Blackwell's Supermarket. Use the information in the leaflet to answer the questions.

Run for the sun... with Blackwell's new range of sun products.

Sun cream – SPF 10	£4.50
Cream – SPF 15	£5.50
Lotion – SPF 15	£4.50
Spray – SPF 20	£6.50
Block – SPF 30	£5.95
After-sun milk	£4.95

tutor questions

1. How much does the SPF 10 sun cream cost?
2. How much more does the SPF 15 sun cream cost than the SPF 10 cream?
3. How much does the sun spray cost?
4. Which is the most expensive item of sun care?
5. Which is the cheapest item of sun care?

Carry out a survey of your own. Go to a local supermarket and note the names of five sun care products and how much they cost. If you have access to the Internet, you may be able to carry out this task online.
Present your findings using a table.

Use this data showing sales of movies on 13th July to construct a pictogram in the space below. Choose from these letters to represent each type of disk.

	DVDs	Blue Rays
Action	20	3
Romance	15	1
Comedy	5	1
Children's	8	2

You are going to conduct a survey about buying music. Ask 20 people these questions, and tally their answers.

1. Do you buy music?	Yes	No
2. Do you buy music on CD or download?	CD	Download
3. Do you ever buy music at the supermarket?	Yes	No

4. How many CDs or downloads do you buy each year?				
0	1–5	6–10	11–20	More than 20

5. What type of music do you prefer to buy?				
Chart	Pop	Classical	Country and western	Other

Present the answers to questions 1–3 in a table. Present the answers to questions 4 and 5 as two bar charts.

38. Supermarket – sorting people

Sort and classify objects using two criteria.

This staff list is in alphabetical order. The personnel department needs to sort out the data according to which department each person works for and whether they are male or female. Use the information in the list to create a table to display this data.

Adeyo, Fred Mr	Assistant	Deli counter
Airdrie, Bob Mr	Assistant	Bakery
Bracelin, Rachel Miss	Assistant	Garage
Chandra, Nita Mrs	Assistant	Fish counter
Chen, Bill Mr	Bakery manager	Bakery
Cook, Damian Mr	Assistant	Checkouts
Darwen, Nick Mr	Assistant	Garage
Franks, Debbie Ms	Shelf stacker	Groceries
Graham, Sally Ms	Personnel manager	Personnel department
Gordon, Brenda Mrs	Clerk	Finance department
Gourlay, Mike, Mr	Supervisor	Checkouts
Harding, Julie Mrs	Assistant	Checkouts
Jones, Penny Mrs	Assistant	Checkouts
Jones, Sheila Miss	Finance director	Finance department
Price, Gwen Miss	Clerk	Personnel department
Rust, Jen Ms	Assistant	Customer services
Slater, Ann Miss	Assistant	Deli counter
Smith, Annie Mrs	Supervisor	Fish counter
Soper, Andrew Mr	Assistant	Customer services
Wilkinson, Richard Mr	Assistant	Checkouts

Sort and classify objects using two criteria.

These goods have been left at the tills and need to be put back in the fresh produce department. You need to decide if the goods are fruits or vegetables and if they should be placed in the loose fruits or vegetables section or the pre-weighed fruits and vegetables section. Use the chart to mark your answers.

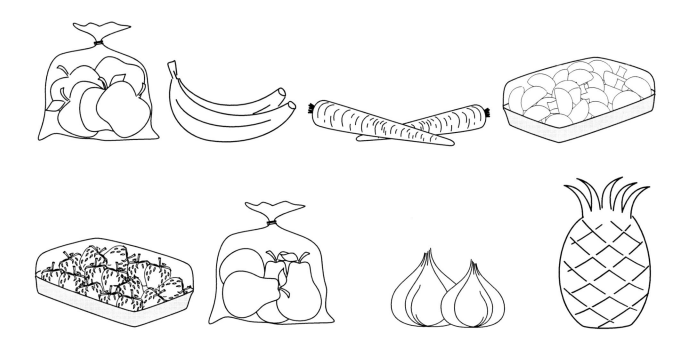

	Fruit	**Vegetable**
Loose		
Pre-pack		

40. Factory – staff training

Represent information in a timetable.

Ten members of the production team at AutoParts are going on a two-day team-building session at a hotel in Swansea. The Personnel Manager sends all the staff a timetable. Transfer this information about the training to the table.

All staff should meet at AutoParts reception at 8 am on Monday 3rd November. Please sign the sheet at reception to say that you are leaving the factory. The minibus leaves at quarter past eight. It will take about three quarters of an hour to reach the hotel in Newport. Each day the training sessions will start at 9.15 am. There are two half hour coffee breaks – one at 10.45 and the other at 3.15. Lunch will be served at 12.45 and training resumes at half past one. On Monday the training session ends at 5 o'clock. You will be expected to meet up in the bar at 7 o'clock. Dinner will be at 8. On Tuesday the session will end at half past four. You should be back at the factory by five thirty.

Date/Time	Action	Notes

HD1/E2.5, MSS1/E2.3, MSS1/E2.4, Rt/E2.1, Wt/E2.1,

skillbuilders ■ handling data ■ entry level 2

The staff at the factory work up to 40 hours a week. Some work part-time. Use the information in the table to answer the questions.

Job title	No. of staff	Hours per week
Welder	4	40
Electrician	2	40
Reception staff	2	25
Cleaner	2	15
Cook	2	20
Canteen assistant	4	20
Accountant	1	37
Secretary	3	37
Sales manager	2	40

1. How many full-time jobs are shown on this table
   (full time = 37 hours per week or more)?   _____

2. How many part-time jobs are shown on this table   _____

3. How many members of staff are shown on this table altogether?   _____

4. How many hours does a cook work?   _____

5. How many more hours does a welder work than a canteen assistant? _____

6. How many more hours does a secretary work than a cleaner?   _____

7. How many fewer hours does a cleaner work than a sales manager? _____

8. How many fewer hours does a cleaner work than an accountant?   _____

42. Factory – top of the league

Extract information from a table. Construct a pictogram.

The factory has a darts team. They play in the local pub league. Their local is the Crown. This table shows how many games have been won. Use the information in the table to answer the questions.

Red Lion	Black Bull	Crown	Ship	Anchor
✔	✔	✔	✔	✔
✔	✔	✔	✔	✔
✔	✔	✔	✔	
	✔	✔	✔	
	✔		✔	
			✔	
			✔	

tutor questions

1. Which team has won the most games?
2. How many games has the Ship team won?
3. Which team has won the least number of games?
4. How many games has the Red Lion team won?
5. How many more games has the Black Bull won than the Anchor?

Present this information as a pictogram. Choose from these icons to represent each pub team.

Extract information from a list. Construct a table.

The factory has a darts team. They play in the local pub league. This is a list of the fixtures for August and September. Use the information in the list to answer the questions.

12th August	the Black Bull at home to	the Ship
14th August	the Red Lion at home to	the Crown
19th August	the Anchor at home to	the Red Lion
21st August	the Crown at home to	the Anchor
26th August	the Ship at home to	the Black Bull
28th August	the Black Bull at home to	the Red Lion
2nd September	the Red Lion at home to	the Anchor
4th September	the Anchor at home to	the Crown
9th September	the Crown at home to	the Black Bull
12th September	the Ship at home to	the Anchor

tutor questions

1. On what dates did the team from the Red Lion play at home?

2. On what dates did the team from the Anchor play away?

3. Which teams played on 28th August?

4. Which teams played on 12th September?

5. When did the team from the Anchor play?

6. When did the team from the Crown play?

Present the information about fixtures in a table.

Extract information from pictograms.

Use the information from this pictogram to answer the questions.

Distance AutoParts production workers live from work

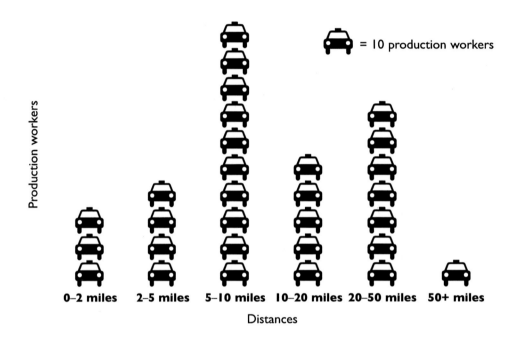

= 10 production workers

Production workers

0–2 miles   2–5 miles   5–10 miles   10–20 miles   20–50 miles   50+ miles

Distances

tutor questions

1. What information does the pictogram give you?

2. What does 🚕 represent?

3. How many production workers live less than 2 miles away from work?

4. How many production workers live between 20-50 miles away from work?

5. How many production workers live more than 50 miles away from work?

6. How many more production workers live between 20-50 miles away from work than those who live 2-5 miles away?

7. Express the number of workers who live 10-20 miles away from work as a fraction of those who live 5-10 miles away.

8. How many production workers are there altogether?

Extract information from bar charts.

Use the information from these charts to answer the questions.

Methods of transport used by AutoParts production workers to get to work

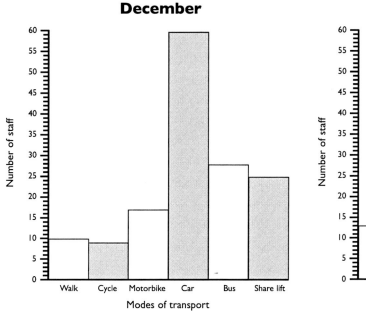

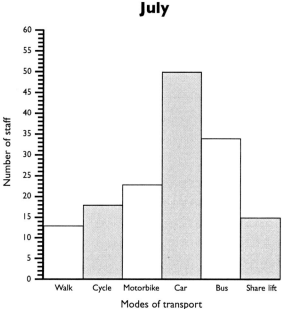

tutor questions

1. What information does the bar chart give you?

2. How many methods of transport are listed?

3. How many production workers walk to work in December?

4. How many production workers cycle to work in July?

5. How many production workers take the bus to work in December?

6. How many production workers share a lift to work in July?

7. How many more production workers travel by motorbike to work in July compared to December?

8. How many fewer production workers drive their car to work in July compared to December?

9. Why do you think there are differences between workers' modes of transport in December and July?

Use the information from this AutoParts canteen menu to answer the questions on Worksheet 47.

AUTOPARTS
Menu

Tea – cup	50 p
Tea – mug	75 p
Coffee – cup	60 p
Coffee – mug	85 p
Hot chocolate	90 p
Juice	65 p
Beans on toast	£1.50
Eggs on toast	£1.50
Soup and a roll	£1.25
Brunch	£3.00
Main meal of the day (roast + 2 veg)	£3.75
Pudding of the day	75 p
Sandwiches (white/brown)	£2.50
Chips	£1.00
Bacon bap	£1.50
Sausage bap	£1.75
Toasted teacake	£1.00

Extract information from lists.

47

1. How much does a cup of coffee cost?   _____

2. How much does a portion of chips cost?   _____

3. How much does a main meal cost?   _____

4. How much does a hot chocolate cost?   _____

5. How much does a sausage bap cost?   _____

6. How much does a pudding cost?   _____

7. What is the most expensive item on the menu?   _____

8. What is the cheapest item on the menu?   _____

9. How many drinks are on the menu?   _____

10. How many food items are on the menu?   _____

Extract information from a block graph.

Use the information in the graph to answer the questions.

Number of crisps sold from restroom vending machine on 15th September

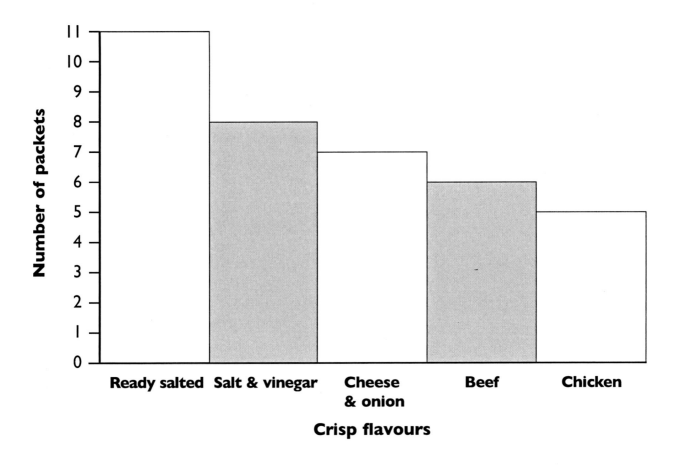

tutor questions

1. How many packets of ready salted flavour crisps were sold?
2. How many packets of salt and vinegar flavour crisps were sold?
3. How many packets of cheese and onion flavour crisps were sold?
4. How many packets of beef flavour crisps were sold?
5. How many packets of chicken flavour crisps were sold?
6. How many more ready salted flavour crisps were sold than chicken flavour?
7. How many more ready salted flavour crisps were sold than beef flavour?

Extract data from tables. Count tally marks. Construct a block graph.

This chart shows how many of each of these items were used on Production Line 1 on the week beginning Monday 18 August. Use the information to complete the tasks.

	Nuts (1 inch)	Washers (rubber)	Panel pins	Rivets	Screws (4 inch)
Monday	ⅣⅣ ⅣⅣ ‖	ⅣⅣ ⅣⅣ	ⅣⅣ ‖‖	ⅣⅣ ⅣⅣ ⅣⅣ ⅣⅣ ‖‖‖‖	ⅣⅣ ⅣⅣ
Tuesday	ⅣⅣ ⅣⅣ	ⅣⅣ ⅣⅣ ‖	ⅣⅣ ⅣⅣ	ⅣⅣ ⅣⅣ ‖	ⅣⅣ ⅣⅣ ‖‖
Wednesday	ⅣⅣ ⅣⅣ	ⅣⅣ ⅣⅣ ⅣⅣ ⅣⅣ ‖	ⅣⅣ ⅣⅣ ‖	ⅣⅣ ‖‖‖‖	ⅣⅣ ⅣⅣ ‖‖‖‖
Thursday	ⅣⅣ ⅣⅣ ⅣⅣ ⅣⅣ ⅣⅣ ‖‖‖	ⅣⅣ ⅣⅣ ‖‖	ⅣⅣ ⅣⅣ ⅣⅣ ⅣⅣ ⅣⅣ ⅣⅣ	ⅣⅣ ⅣⅣ ⅣⅣ ⅣⅣ ⅣⅣ ‖‖‖	ⅣⅣ ⅣⅣ ⅣⅣ ‖
Friday	ⅣⅣ ⅣⅣ ‖‖‖‖	ⅣⅣ ⅣⅣ ‖‖‖	ⅣⅣ ⅣⅣ ⅣⅣ	ⅣⅣ ⅣⅣ	ⅣⅣ ⅣⅣ ⅣⅣ ‖‖‖
Total					

1. Total each tally up and write your answer in the column.

2. Check your answer with a calculator.

3. Draw a block graph to show how many spare parts were used on Production Line 1 last week. Give your graph a title. Make sure you label each axis.

50. Factory – sorting people

Sort and classify objects using two criteria.

This staff list is in alphabetical order. The personnel department needs to sort out the data according to which department each person works for and whether they are full-time or part-time. Use the information in the list to create a table to display this data.

Brace, David	Fork lift truck driver	Warehouse department	full-time
Brady, Tony	Assistant	Spare parts department	part-time
Brightman, Helen	Personnel manager	Personnel department	full-time
Cannon, Mike	Forklift truck driver	Warehouse department	full-time
Davies, Tony	Welder	Engineering department	full-time
Evans, Gareth	Admin clerk	Finance department	part-time
Johal, Asif	Engineer	Engineering department	full-time
Jolly, Bob	Driver	Warehouse department	full-time
Jones, Dan	Welder	Engineering department	full-time
Kelly, Mike	Assistant	Spare parts department	full-time
Lincoln, Mandy	Clerk	Personnel department	part-time
Lowe, Jane	Production supervisor	Production department	full-time
Manning, Ingrid	Regional sales co-ordinator	Sales department	full-time
Nason, Justin	Sales manager	Sales department	full-time
Oakley, Jim	Warehouse manager	Warehouse department	full-time
Prytherch, Sue	Admin clerk	Sales department	part-time
Rana, Sanjay	Production worker	Production department	full-time
Russell, Gemma	Production worker	Production department	part-time
Salter, Mo	Production worker	Production department	full-time
Tombs, Debbie	Production worker	Production department	part-time

Sort and classify objects using two criteria.

These spare parts need to be stored so that staff can find them easily. Devise a way of labelling the drawers so that all the parts are easy to find. There are not enough drawers for each item to have its own space.

Washer 50 mm metal
Washer 25 mm metal
Washer 25 mm plastic
Washer 50 mm plastic
Steel panel pins 25 mm
Steel panel pins 50 mm

Steel screws 50 mm
Steel screws 75 mm
Steel rivets 15 mm
Steel rivets 25 mm
Aluminium rivets 10 mm
Aluminium rivets 25 mm

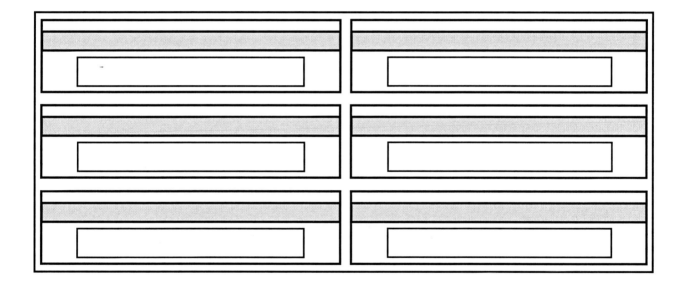

2. How to read tables 1

1. It will cost £5.50 to send a parcel weighing 4 kg.
2. It will cost £4.50 to send a parcel weighing 3 kg.
3. It will cost £9.50 to send a parcel weighing 8 kg.
4. It will cost £7.50 to send a parcel weighing 6 kg.
5. It will cost £8.50 to send a parcel weighing 7 kg.
6. It will cost £6.50 to send a parcel weighing 5 kg.

3. How to read tables 2

1. 6 kg
2. 1 kg
3. 4 kg
4. 7 kg
5. 3 kg
6. 8 kg
7. 2 kg
8. 5 kg

5. How to read information in block graphs 2

1. 15 people
2. 20 people
3. 25 people
4. 30 people
5. 10 people
6. car
7. bicycle

7. Where can it go? 2

Sorted by size and shape:

Category	Number
Large circle	9
Small circle	14
Large triangle	10
Small triangle	10

Sorted by size and colour:

Category	Number
Large shaded	9
Small shaded	13

Sorted by shape and colour:

Category	Number
Shaded circle	11
Un-shaded circle	12
Shaded triangle	11
Un-shaded triangle	9

8. Data everywhere 1

1. Married 9
   Single 13
2. Male 15
   Female 13
3. Driver 9
   Non-driver 7
4. Employed 14
   Not employed 7

9. Data everywhere 2

You should check your answers with your teacher.

11. Show it off 2

1. diagram/map
2. list
3. table
4. pictogram
5. diagram

12. How to label a block graph

1. Vertical axis: centimetres, horizontal axis: months.
2. Vertical axis: hours, horizontal axis: months.
3. Vertical axis: number, horizontal axis: accommodation.

13. How to construct a block graph

1. Number of staff birthdays per month
2. Number of staff on holiday each month
3. Staff's lunchtime habits over a month

14. Hotel – guest survey

Tutor questions
1. The title of the chart is "Number of guests who stayed at the Old Hall Hotel from 6th to 12th October".
2. 16
3. Friday
4. Thursday
5. 4
6. Tuesday and Wednesday

15. Hotel – laundry bar chart

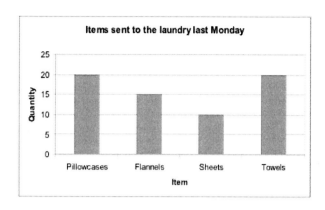

16. Hotel – housekeeping bar chart

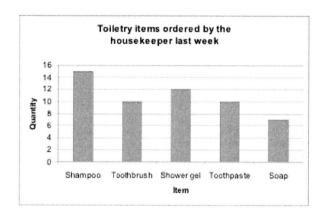

17. Hotel – keeping the customers happy

1.

Guest	Room size	Cleanliness	Room service	Meals	Value for money	Porter service	Would you revisit?
Totals	⊤⊦⊦ I	⊤⊦⊦ IIII	⊤⊦⊦ IIII	⊤⊦⊦ IIII	⊤⊦⊦ II	⊤⊦⊦ I	⊤⊦⊦ IIII

2.

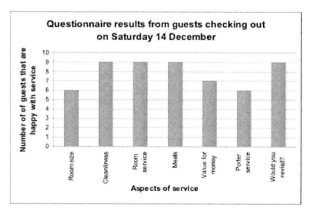

18. Hotel – leisure club use 1

	Pool	Jacuzzi	Sauna	Weights	Studio
Monday	17	9	9	4	2
Tuesday	9	7	7	3	0
Wednesday	9	8	4	0	0
Thursday	9	9	7	3	0
Friday	19	14	9	9	4
Saturday	20	17	13	16	19
Sunday	14	9	16	7	4

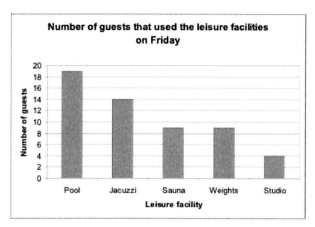

19. Hotel – leisure club use 2

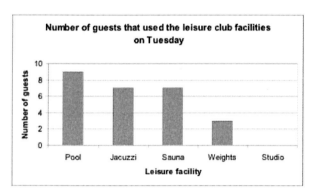

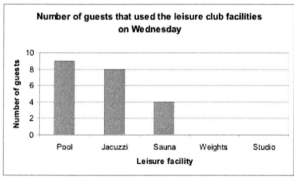

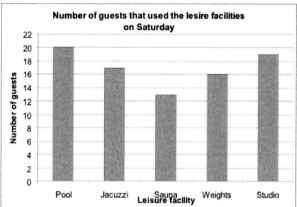

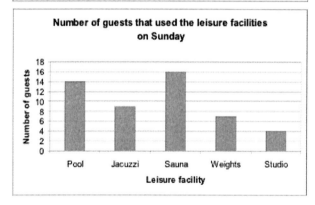

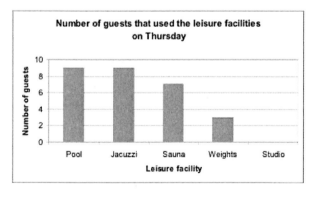

20. Hotel – the mystery tour

Time	Action	Notes
9 a.m.	Meet in lobby	Check tickets
9.15	Bus leaves	Will take an hour
10.15	Arrive at destination	
12 p.m.	Lunch	
3 p.m.	Bus leaves for hotel	
4 p.m.	Arrive at hotel	

Answers

21. Hotel – keep fit classes

Activity	Tally	Total
Aerobics	~~卌~~ ~~卌~~ |||	13
Swimming	~~卌~~ ||||	9
Tennis	~~卌~~		6

Aerobics	13 hours
Swimming	9 hours
Tennis	6 hours

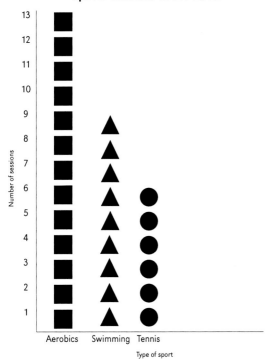

Pictogram to show number of sports sessions at the hotel

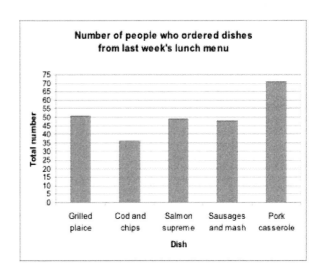

22. Hotel – lunch menu 1

Main meal	Total for the week
Grilled plaice	51
Cod and chips	36
Salmon supreme	49
Sausages and mash	48
Pork casserole	71

23. Hotel – lunch menu 2

1. Pork casserole
2. Cod and chips
3. Sunday
4. Monday
5. Wednesday and Friday
6. 48 dishes
7. 51 dishes

	Yes	No
1. Help the chef plan what produce he needs to order	✔	
2. Help the chef decide what puddings to prepare		✔
3. Help the restaurant manager plan how many waiters to employ		✔
4. Help customers to decide what to order		✔
5. Help the chef decide what meal to take off the menu	✔	
6. Help the chef decide how large the portions should be		✔

24–25. Hotel – lunch survey 1–2

You should check your answers with your teacher.

26. Hotel – sorting people

Department	Name	Job title	Permanent?	Temporary
Sales team	Baines, Denise	Promotions manager	✔	
Restaurant	Boyer, Henri	Wine waiter	✔	
Restaurant	Falstaff, John	Waiter		✔
Restaurant	Fitzpatrick, Steve	Waiter	✔	
Restaurant	Green, Liam	Wine waiter	✔	
Restaurant	Mullins, Debbie	Catering manager	✔	
Restaurant	Pezzy, Sarah	Waitress		✔
Restaurant	Potter, Linda	Waitress	✔	
Leisure Club	Bromley, Maxine	Manager	✔	
Leisure Club	Davies, Jack	Instructor	✔	
Leisure Club	Jenkins, Laura	Beauty therapist		✔
Housekeeping	Callington, Edith	Housekeeper	✔	
Housekeeping	Holland, Bob	Porter	✔	
Housekeeping	Pace, Julie	Cleaner	✔	
Housekeeping	Roberts, Louise	Chambermaid		✔
Housekeeping	Smith, Valerie	Cleaner		✔
Housekeeping	Wu, Li	Chambermaid	✔	
Kitchen	Hardy, Alex	Cook	✔	
Kitchen	Jones, Val	Chef		✔
Kitchen	Nedding, Dolly	Kitchen hand		✔
Kitchen	Nunn, Irene	Cook	✔	
Kitchen	Smith, Kevin	Chef	✔	
Kitchen	Vautier, Jean-Claude	Chef	✔	
Kitchen	Vine, Maureen	Cook	✔	
Kitchen	Wall, Jane	Cook	✔	
Front of house	Leblanc, Anthony	Receptionist		✔
Front of house	Lyons, Jo	Receptionist	✔	
Bar	Menendez, Juan	Bar manager	✔	
Bar	Othen, Jen	Bar staff		✔
Bar	Patel, Dev	Bar staff	✔	
Management	Clarke, Nick		✔	
Management	Goodman, Julie	Personnel manager	✔	

27. Hotel – organising rooms

Type	Number of rooms	Moorland view	Garden view	Floor
Double bedroom	2	✔		First floor
Double bedroom	2		✔	First floor
Double bedroom	3	✔		Second floor
Double bedroom	2		✔	Second floor
Double bedroom	5	✔		Annexe
Double bedroom	5		✔	Annexe
Single bedroom	1	✔		First floor
Single bedroom	1		✔	Second floor
Single bedroom	2	✔		Annexe
Single bedroom	2		✔	Annexe
Twin bedroom	1		✔	First floor
Twin bedroom	1	✔		Second floor
Twin bedroom	1		✔	Annexe
Family	1		✔	First floor
Family	1	✔		First floor
Family	2		✔	Annexe
Family	1	✔		Annexe

28. Supermarket – staff training

Time	Action	Notes
9 am	Meet at supermarket car park	Check off list
9.15 am	Coach leaves	
10.30 am	Arrive at Lancashire County Training	
11 am	Training begins	Need to register first
1 pm	Lunch break	
2 pm	Back for training	
4 pm	Training finishes	Collect certificates as you leave
4.15 pm	Coaches leave	
5.30 pm	Back at Blackwell's	

29. Supermarket – daily dairy count

1.

Type of cheese	Kilos sold	Total
Cheddar	|||| |||| |||| ||	17
Edam	|||| ||||	10
Stilton	|||| |||| |||| |||| ||||	24
Ricotta	||||		6
Brie	|||| |||| |||	13

2.

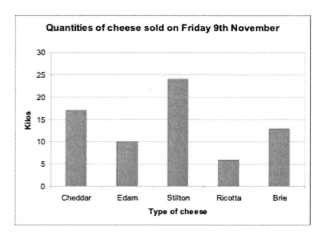

30. Supermarket – daily toiletries count

Type of shampoo	Bottles sold	Total
Blackwell's anti-dandruff	ℕℕ IIII	14
Blackwell's frequent use	ℕℕ ℕℕ ℕℕ I	31
Blackwell's medicated	ℕ IIII	9
Blackwell's extra body	ℕℕ ℕℕ ℕℕ II	27
Blackwell's supersoft	ℕℕ ℕℕ III	18

2.

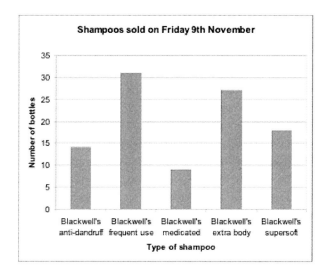

31. Supermarket – daily groceries count

1.

Type of soup	Cans sold	Total
Blackwell's chicken	ℕℕ ℕℕ ℕℕ ℕ II	37
Blackwell's tomato	ℕℕ ℕℕ ℕℕ ℕℕ IIII	44
Blackwell's mushroom	ℕℕ ℕℕ ℕ I	26
Blackwell's oxtail	ℕℕ ℕℕ III	23
Blackwell's French onion	ℕℕ ℕℕ ℕ I	26

2. Cans of soup sold on Friday 9th November

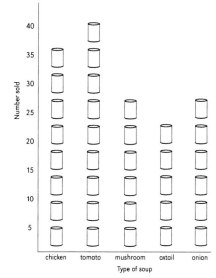

32. Supermarket – frozen favourites

Tutor questions
1. Numbers of cartons of Blackwell's own brand of ice cream sold on 4th July
2. 5
3. 80 cartons
4. 30 cartons
5. 10 cartons
6. 40 cartons
7. 50 cartons
8. 260 cartons
You should check the findings of your survey with your teacher.

33. Supermarket – staffing

Tutor questions
1. Number of workers in-store at 10 am on 27th July
2. 6
3. 13
4. 5
5. 1
6. There are 3 less cleaners than bakery section staff.
7. 6
You should check the findings of your survey with your teacher.

34. Supermarket – sales figures

Tutor questions
1. The pictogram gives information about the sales figures for 14th October.
2. It represents £100.
3. £500
4. £100
5. £800
6. £300
7. £400
8. £2600

35. Supermarket – sun protection

1. £4.50
2. £1.00
3. £6.50
4. The SPF 20 sun spray.
5. The SPF 10 sun cream and the SPF 15 sun lotion.
You should check the findings of your survey with your teacher.

36. Supermarket – movie magic

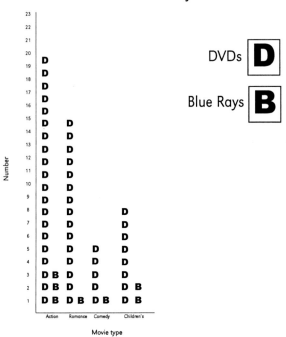

Pictogram to show the sales of movies on 13th July

DVDs **D**

Blue Rays **B**

37. Supermarket – buying music

You should check the findings of your survey with your teacher.

38. Supermarket – sorting people

Department	Name	Job title	Male	Female
Deli counter	Adeyo, Fred Mr	Assistant	✔	
Deli counter	Slater, Ann Miss	Assistant		✔
Bakery	Airdrie, Bob Mr	Assistant	✔	
Bakery	Chen, Bill Mr	Bakery manager	✔	
Garage	Bracelin, Rachel Miss	Assistant		✔
Garage	Darwen, Nick Mr	Assistant	✔	
Fish counter	Chandra, Nita Miss	Assistant		✔
Fish counter	Smith, Annie Mrs	Supervisor		✔
Checkouts	Cook, Damian Mr	Assistant	✔	
Checkouts	Gourlay, Mike Mr	Supervisor	✔	
Checkouts	Harding, Julie Mrs	Assistant		✔
Checkouts	Jones, Penny Mrs	Assistant		✔
Checkouts	Wilkinson, Richard Mr	Assistant	✔	
Groceries	Franks, Debbie Ms	Shelf stacker		✔
Personnel department	Graham, Sally Ms	Personnel manager		✔
Personnel department	Price, Gwen Miss	Clerk		✔
Finance department	Gordon, Brenda Mrs	Clerk		✔
Finance department	Jones, Sheila Miss	Finance director		✔
Customer services	Rust, Jen Ms	Assistant		✔
Customer services	Soper, Andrew Mr	Assistant	✔	

39. Supermarket – organising returns

	Fruit	Vegetable
Loose	bananas pineapples	carrots garlic
Pre-pack	apples strawberries pears	mushrooms

40. Factory – staff training

Date/Time	Action	Notes
8 am 3rd November	Meet at AutoParts reception	Sign sheet to say you're leaving factory
8.15 am 3rd November	Mini bus leaves	Will take 45 minutes
9 am 3rd November	Arrive at hotel in Newport	
9.15 am 3rd and 4th November	Training session starts	
10.45 am 3rd and 4th November	Coffee break	
11.15 am 3rd and 4th November	Back to training session	
12.45 pm 3rd and 4th November	Lunch	
1.30 pm 3rd and 4th November	Training resumes	
3.15 pm 3rd and 4th November	Coffee break	
3.45 pm 3rd and 4th November	Back to training session	
5 pm 3rd November	Training session ends	
7 pm 3rd November	Meet in bar	
8 pm 3rd November	Dinner	
4.30 pm 4th November	Training session ends	
5.30 pm 4th November	Back at AutoParts	

41. Factory – who works the most?

1. 12
2. 4
3. 22
4. 20 hours
5. 20 hours
6. 22 hours
7. 25 hours
8. 22 hours

42. Factory – top of the league

Tutor questions
1. The Ship
2. 7
3. The Anchor
4. 3
5. 3

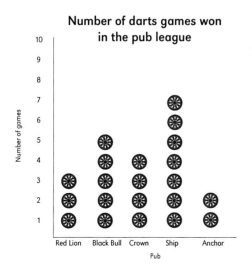

Number of darts games won in the pub league

43. Factory – league fixtures

Tutor questions
1. 14th August and 2nd September
2. 21st August and 2nd September
3. The Black Bull and the Red Lion
4. The Ship and the Anchor
5. 19th August, 21st August, 2nd September, 4th September and 12th September
6. 14th August, 21st August, 4th September and 9th September

Date	Home	Away
12th August	Black Bull	Ship
14th August	Red Lion	Crown
19th August	Anchor	Red Lion
21st August	Crown	Anchor
26th August	Ship	Black Bull
28th August	Black Bull	Red Lion
2nd September	Red Lion	Anchor
4th September	Anchor	Crown
9th September	Crown	Black Bull
12th September	Ship	Anchor

44. Factory – distance from work

Tutor questions
1. The pictogram shows the distance that AutoParts production workers live from work.
2. It represents 10 production workers.
3. 30
4. 70
5. 10
6. 30
7. $5/10$
8. 300

45. Factory – transport to work

Tutor questions
1. The bar chart shows the methods of transport

used by AutoParts production workers to get to work in July and December.

2. 6

3. 10

4. 18

5. 28

6. 15

7. 11

8. 10

9. There are differences between workers' modes of transport in December and January probably because the weather is much colder in December so fewer people walk to or cycle to work.

47. Factory – canteen menu 2

1. 60p

2. £1.00

3. £3.75

4. 90p

5. £1.75

6. 75p

7. Main meal

8. Cup of tea

9. 6

10. 11

48. Factory – vending machine sales

Tutor questions

1. 11

2. 8

3. 7

4. 6

5. 5

6. 6

7. 5

49. Factory – stockcheck

	Nuts (1 inch)	Washers (rubber)	Panel pins	Rivets	Screws (4 inch)
Monday	ꐼꐼ II	ꐼ ꐼ	ꐼ III	ꐼ ꐼ ꐼ ꐼ IIII	ꐼ ꐼ
Tuesday	ꐼ ꐼ	ꐼ ꐼ I	ꐼ ꐼ	ꐼ ꐼ I	ꐼ ꐼ II
Wednesday	ꐼ ꐼ	ꐼ ꐼ ꐼ ꐼ I	ꐼ ꐼ I	ꐼ IIII	ꐼ ꐼ IIII
Thursday	ꐼ ꐼ ꐼ ꐼ ꐼ III	ꐼ ꐼ II	ꐼ ꐼ ꐼ ꐼ ꐼ ꐼ	ꐼ ꐼ ꐼ III I	ꐼ ꐼ ꐼ
Friday	ꐼ ꐼ IIII	ꐼ ꐼ III	ꐼ ꐼ ꐼ	ꐼ ꐼ	ꐼ ꐼ ꐼ III
Total	74	67	74	82	70

3.

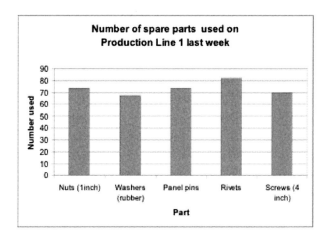

50. Factory – sorting people

Department	Name	Job Title	Full time	Part time
Warehouse	Brace, David	Fork lift truck driver	✔	
Warehouse	Cannon, Mike	Fork lift truck driver	✔	
Warehouse	Jolly, Bob	Driver	✔	
Warehouse	Oakley, Jim	Warehouse manager	✔	
Spare parts	Brady, Tony	Assistant		✔
Spare parts	Kelly, Mike	Assistant	✔	
Personnel	Brightman, Helen	Personnel manager	✔	
Personnel	Lincoln, Mandy	Clerk		✔
Engineering	Davies, Tony	Welder	✔	
Engineering	Johal, Asif	Engineer	✔	
Engineering	Jones, Dan	Welder	✔	
Finance	Evans, Gareth	Admin Clerk		✔
Production	Lowe, Jane	Production supervisor	✔	
Production	Rana, Sanjay	Production worker	✔	
Production	Russell, Gemma	Production worker		✔
Production	Salter, Mo	Production worker	✔	
Production	Tombs, Debbie	Production worker		✔
Sales	Manning, Ingrid	Regional sales co-ordinator	✔	
Sales	Nason, Justin	Sales manager	✔	
Sales	Prytherch, Sue	Admin clerk		✔

51. Factory – organising parts

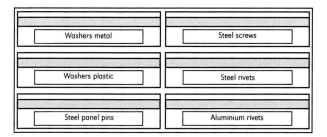

Activity index

Carry out surveys	9, 24, 32, 33, 35, 37
Construct block graphs	15, 16, 17, 19, 22, 24, 29, 30, 32, 33, 37, 49
Count tally marks	18, 21, 29, 30, 31, 49
Extract data from lists	26, 27, 38, 43, 50
Extract data from price lists	35, 46, 47
Extract data from block graphs/bar charts	4, 5, 14, 23, 25, 33, 45, 48
Extract data from pictograms	32, 33, 44
Extract data from tables	2, 3, 17, 21, 22, 23, 25, 36, 41, 42, 49
Give a block graph a title	13
Label axes on a block graph	12
Present data in a pictogram	21, 31, 36, 42
Present data in a table	24, 32, 33, 35, 37, 43
Present data in a timetable	20, 28, 40
Sort and classify objects using two criteria	6, 7, 26, 27, 38, 39, 50, 51
Understand different ways to present data	1, 10, 11
Use tally charts to collect data	8, 9, 18, 21, 29

Handling Data entry level 2 – Curriculum elements matrix

Handling Data elements

HD1/E2 – Data and statistical measures

HD1/E2.1 – *extract information from lists, tables, simple diagrams and black graphs*
Worksheets – 2, 3, 4, 5, 10, 11, 12, 13, 14, 17, 18, 19, 21, 22, 23, 25, 27, 32, 33, 34, 35, 36, 37, 41, 42, 43, 44, 45, 46, 47, 48 and 51.

HD1/E2.2 – *make numerical comparisons from block graphs*
Worksheets – 14, 22, 23, 25, 32, 33, 34, 35, 36, 44, 45 and 48.

HD1/E2.3 – *sort and classify objects using two criteria*
Worksheets – 6, 7, 26, 27, 38, 39, 50 and 51.

HD1/E2.4 – *collect simple numerical information*
Worksheets – 8, 9, 21, 24, 32, 33, 35, 36 and 37.

HD1/E2.5 – *represent information so that it makes sense to others (e.g. in lists, tables and diagrams)*
Worksheets – 1, 11, 12, 13, 15, 16, 17, 18, 19, 20, 21, 22, 24, 26, 27, 28, 29, 30, 31, 32, 33, 35, 36, 37, 38, 40, 41, 42, 43 and 49.

Number elements

N1/E2 – Whole numbers

N1/E2.1 – *count reliably up to 20 items*
Worksheets – 6, 7, 8, 9, 14, 15, 16, 17, 18, 19, 21, 29, 30, 31, 32, 42, 44, 45, 46, 47 and 49.

N1/E2.2 – *read, write, order and compare numbers up to 100*
Worksheets – 2, 3, 4, 5, 6, 7, 8, 9, 14, 15, 16, 17, 18, 19, 21, 22, 23, 29, 30, 31, 32, 41, 42, 44, 45 and 49.

N1/E2.3 – *add and subtract two-digit whole numbers*
Worksheets – 22, 32, 41, 44 and 45.

N2/E2 – Fractions, decimals and percentages

N2/E2.2 – *find halves and quarters of small numbers of items or shapes*
Worksheets – 44 and 45.

Measures, shape and space elements

MSS1/E2 – Common measures

MSS1/E2.3 – *read and record time in common date format*
Worksheets – 40 and 43.

MSS1/E2.4 – *read and understand time displayed on analogue and 12-hour digital clocks in hours, half hours and quarter hours*
Worksheets – 28 and 40.

MSS2/E2 – Shape and space

MSS2/E2.1 – *recognise and name 2-D and 3-D shapes*

Worksheets – 6 and 7.

Reading elements

Rt/E2 – Text focus

Rt/E2.1 – *trace and understand the main events of chronological and instructional texts*
Worksheets – 2, 3, 4, 5, 6, 7, 8, 9, 20, 25, 26, 27, 28, 38, 40, 43 and 50.

Rw/E1 – Word focus

Rw/E1.1 – *possess a limited, meaningful sight vocabulary of words, signs and symbols*
Worksheets – 46 and 47.

Rw/E2 – Word focus

Rw/E2.2 – *recognise high-frequency words and words with common spelling patterns*
Worksheet – 14.

Writing elements

Wt/E2 – Writing comprehension

Wt/E1.1 – *use written words and phrases to record or present information*
Worksheets – 46 and 47.

Wt/E2.1 – *use written words and phrases to record or present information*
Worksheets – 4, 5, 14, 20, 25, 26, 27, 28, 38, 39, 40, 43, 45 and 50.

Ww/E2.1 – *spell correctly the majority of personal details and familiar common words*
Worksheet – 14.

Ww/E2.3 – *produce legible text*
Worksheet – 14.

	Grilled plaice	Cod and chips	Salmon supreme	Sausages and mash	Pork casserole
Monday	3	1	2	0	6
Tuesday	4	3	12	6	3
Wednesday	2	6	4	10	12
Thursday	10	3	7	5	8
Friday	4	3	7	10	10
Saturday	12	8	8	11	14
Sunday	16	12	9	6	18

Job title	No. of staff	Hours per week
Welder	4	40
Electrician	2	40
Reception staff	2	25
Cleaner	2	15
Cook	2	20
Canteen assistant	4	20
Accountant	1	37
Secretary	3	37
Sales manager	2	40

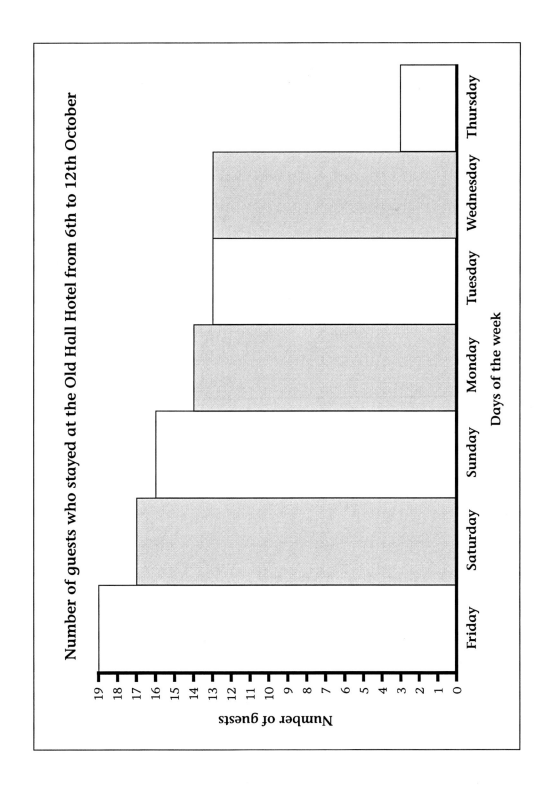

Number of guests who stayed at the Old Hall Hotel from 6th to 12th October

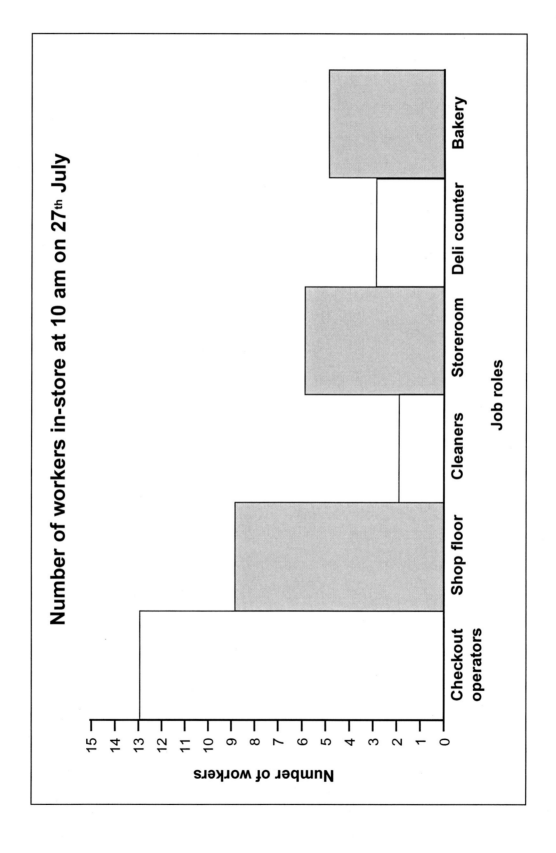

Number of workers in-store at 10 am on 27th July

Adeyo, Fred Mr	Assistant	Deli counter
Airdrie, Bob Mr	Assistant	Bakery
Bracelin, Rachel Miss	Assistant	Garage
Chandra, Nita Mrs	Assistant	Fish counter
Chen, Bill Mr	Bakery manager	Bakery
Cook, Damian Mr	Assistant	Checkouts
Darwen, Nick Mr	Assistant	Garage
Franks, Debbie Ms	Shelf stacker	Groceries
Graham, Sally Ms	Personnel manager	Personnel department
Gordon, Brenda Mrs	Clerk	Finance department
Gourlay, Mike, Mr	Supervisor	Checkouts
Harding, Julie Mrs	Assistant	Checkouts
Jones, Penny Mrs	Assistant	Checkouts
Jones, Sheila Miss	Finance director	Finance department
Price, Gwen Miss	Clerk	Personnel department
Rust, Jen Ms	Assistant	Customer services
Slater, Ann Miss	Assistant	Deli counter
Smith, Annie Mrs	Supervisor	Fish counter
Soper, Andrew Mr	Assistant	Customer services
Wilkinson, Richard Mr	Assistant	Checkouts

Washer 50 mm metal

Washer 25 mm metal

Washer 25 mm plastic

Washer 50 mm plastic

Steel panel pins 25 mm

Steel panel pins 50 mm

Steel screws 50 mm

Steel screws 75 mm

Steel rivets 15 mm

Steel rivets 25 mm

Aluminium rivets 10 mm

Aluminium rivets 25 mm